This bite-sized book h a useful overview of m following:

- Raise awareness c

- Recognise the importance of getting support if needed

- Be proactive about looking after yourself

- Take on board healthy coping mechanisms

- Support others who may need your help

Mental health needs a great deal of attention. It's the final taboo and it needs to be faced and dealt with

Adam Ant

What is mental health?

Mental health includes your emotional, psychological, and social well-being. It is something that affects how you think, feel, and act. It also determines how well you handle stress, relate to others, and the decisions and choices you make.

There are many factors that contribute to mental health, including:

- Biological factors, such as genes or brain chemistry

- Life experiences, such as trauma or abuse

- Family history of mental health problems

- Lifestyle can also have an impact

- Overexposure to prolonged bouts of stress

Feelings are something you have; not something you are

Shannon L. Alder

How do you know if you have a mental health issue?

- Behaving and feeling like a very different person in a negative way

- Uncharacteristic anxiety, anger, or mood swings

- Social withdrawal and wanting to isolate yourself

- Lack of self-care and personal hygiene

- Behaving in a way that puts yourself or others at risk

- Dependency on unhealthy coping mechanisms

- A sense of hopelessness, deep sadness or feeling overwhelmed

- Sleepless nights

- Panic attacks

- Self-harm

My dark days made me strong.
Or maybe I already was strong,
and they made me prove it

Emery Lord

We are all in it together

It is estimated that one in four people have mental health problems and more and more people are now addressing this. Our own royal family have spearheaded an initiative on mental health called Heads Together. This is a campaign to tackle stigma and change the conversation on mental health with fundraising for a series of innovative new mental health services.

You absolutely do not need to feel alone as people from every walk of life are sharing their personal stories of the challenges that they face. Mental health is something we all have to live with and anyone can be affected.

It doesn't have to take over your life, it doesn't have to define you as a person, it's just important that you ask for help. It's not a sign of weakness

Demi Lovato

Open up and get some support

There is so much support out there and no one needs to feel afraid or ashamed. So many people experience mental health issues that an increasing amount of workplaces now have mental health first-aiders who are on hand to offer support and guidance. Another initiative is Time to Change, which is a growing social movement working to change the way we all think and act about mental health problems.

If you feel as if you have mental health problems it is really important to reach out and talk about it. Opening up and talking about how you feel is the first step to feeling better.

Your doctor will be able to advise on the best course of action and may suggest talking therapies like CBT - Cognitive Behavioural Therapy.

Please note that this bite-sized book is in no way meant to replace the advice of a medical professional, however it does offer a few useful suggestions that may well help you.

Don't be ashamed of your story. It will inspire others

Unknown

Start by doing what's necessary,
then do what's possible;
and suddenly you are doing
the impossible

Saint Francis of Assisi

13

How to look after your mental health

Be your own best friend

Valuing and treating yourself with the kindness and respect you would your own best friend is so important. Giving yourself a hard time and being self-critical about every imperfection and every mistake you make is not helpful. You were not born to be perfect, you were born to be real and real people mess up from time to time and that is perfectly OK. Liking, respecting and looking after yourself is very important in terms of your emotional well-being.

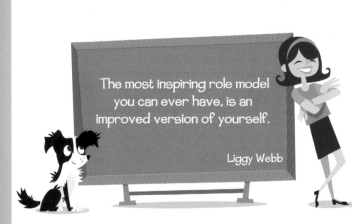

The most inspiring role model you can ever have, is an improved version of yourself.

Liggy Webb

Be your own role model

We are all people in progress and the best and most realistic role model you can ever have is yourself as an improved version. It's exciting that we all have potential to grow as people and whilst self-acceptance is important, it's always motivating to grow as a person and set ourselves challenges. In a world of fake news and fake imagery it is really important to not compare yourself to others. It's unrealistic and there will always be people who are worse off or better off, which will only engender emotions of pity or vanity of which neither is great. You were born to be an original so why would you want to be a copy anyway?

17

It's up to you today to start making healthy choices. Not choices that are just healthy for your body, but healthy for your mind

Steve Maraboli

Manage your stress levels

The World Health Organization has dubbed stress as the modern-day health epidemic.

For a multitude of reasons the pace of modern life has accelerated. In a rapidly evolving world of too much choice and overwhelm it can be challenging to establish a healthy balance. Everyday pressures can build up and affect our stress levels without us even being aware that it is happening. The creep of burnout can be insidious.

Increasing your stress intelligence and how you manage your stress by raising awareness of your stress triggers and responses is key.

Keep active

A sedentary lifestyle isn't helpful when it comes to your personal well-being. Research has now identified that physical inactivity may increase the risks of certain cancers and contribute to anxiety and depression. People who engage in more physical activity are less likely to develop heart disease.

Exercise is vital for maintaining mental fitness, and it can reduce stress. Studies show that it is very effective at reducing fatigue, improving alertness and concentration, and enhancing overall cognitive function.

When stress affects the brain, with its many nerve connections, the rest of the body feels the impact as well. So it stands to reason that if your body feels better, so does your mind. Being active doesn't necessarily mean a trip to the gym, just getting outside in the fresh air for a brisk walk can be very beneficial!

Devices to measure how many steps you walk a day can also be very motivating. Setting yourself a target to walk 10,000 steps a day is recommended for a healthy heart, as well as having positive effects on your mental health too.

Fuel your body

Think of your body as the most magnificent machine and be aware of the quality of the fuel that you put into your system. This can have a big impact on how you perform and indeed how you feel emotionally. Here are five tips:

- Eat plenty of vegetables and fruit
- Consume less sugar
- Avoid artificial and processed food
- Keep hydrated and drink plenty of water
- Minimise caffeine and alcohol

Sleep well

Lack of good quality sleep can affect your memory, judgment and mood. There is a close relationship between sleep and mental health. Living with a mental health problem can affect how well you sleep, and poor sleep can have a negative impact on your mental health.

Five ways to sleep better include the following:

1. Establish a sleeping routine to help your body clock

2. Create a comfortable sleeping environment

3. Make the place you sleep a tech-free place

4. Avoid stimulants before you go to sleep

5. Use mindfulness to help you relax

Sometimes it's okay if the only thing you did today was breathe

Unknown

Practise mindfulness

The term mindfulness comes from Eastern spiritual and religious traditions. It is a very old concept and is a key part of Buddhism and also appears in Hindu writings.

A great deal of scientific research now shows that the mindful approach to stress, anxiety and mental health is a very helpful and popular way of dealing with and diffusing high levels of stress.

Mindfulness refers to being completely in touch with and aware of the present moment, as well as taking a non-evaluative and non-judgemental approach to your inner experience. It is essentially about being present and noticing what is around you. So often, if you are not careful, you can find yourself racing through life in a mad dash and not taking time to stop and really appreciate what is going on around you.

How to be more mindful

There are so many ways that you can live more mindfully. Here are four simple suggestions:

1. Begin each day with a beginner's mind
You can choose the day you want by clearing your mind, consciously letting go of any negativity and baggage and beginning each day with a fresh outlook and an open and uncluttered mind.

2. Choose to be present
Look up and around you, feel your feet on the ground, the air on your skin, the wonderment of your environment. Focus on the present moment and make a conscious effort to absorb yourself in it.

3. Breathe deeply
Take time to do some deep breathing. For a few minutes breathe in to the count of five and out to the count of five. This can help reduce stress and have a very calming effect.

4. Mindful engagement
Be present when you are with other people and really attend to listening to them with your undivided attention.

Done is better than perfect

Sheryl Sandberg

Avoid chasing perfection

Experts tend to define perfectionism as "a combination of excessively high personal standards and overly critical self-evaluations".

Some studies show that constantly chasing perfection may seriously harm your mental health and well-being. Perfectionism occurs when you attach irrational importance to being perfect, hold unrealistic expectations of yourself and punish yourself when you self-evaluate the outcome. Perfection is a journey not a destination and sometimes a mantra of better done than perfect can reduce the relentless pressure you may be putting on yourself and also help you to achieve results.

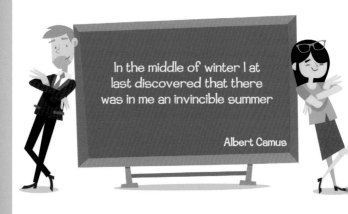

In the middle of winter I at last discovered that there was in me an invincible summer

Albert Camus

Do the things you love doing

It is so important to keep a healthy balance in life with all the things that you do and the people you spend your time with.

Doing things that you are good at can boost your self-esteem and have a positive effect on your mood. Exploring and trying out new hobbies can add interest and distract you from dwelling on negative aspects of your life. It can also connect you to others who share similar interests.

Surrounding yourself with people you love being with is another great way to boost your mood. Stay connected and don't isolate yourself, as being with people can be a real tonic and you can share the things you love doing.

29

Log off

FOMO has been recognised as a recently emerging psychological disorder brought on by the advance of technology. It is an acronym standing for the expression 'fear of missing out'. This is used to describe that feeling of anxiety which many people experience when they discover that other people are having fun together or are being successful at something. Unhealthy and unrealistic comparisons are then made.

FOMO can manifest itself in various ways, from a brief pang of envy through to resentment and a real sense of self-doubt or inadequacy.

Being balanced with your use of technology is so important for mental health and being able to LOG OFF and just give yourself a digital detox can be like giving yourself a mind spa!

Ask for help

Reaching out and seeking help when you need it is not a sign of weakness, it is a sign of strength. We are all on this planet to love and support each other and everyone you meet is facing their own battle. You never really know what is going on in someone else's life and it is important to understand that you never have to feel alone. People who reach out to get appropriate support and care can recover from mental illness and addiction and lead full, rewarding lives and one day you may well have the opportunity to do the same for someone else.

Let the laughter in

Laughter has so many benefits and can be such a great tonic. Even in challenging times it helps to seek out the funny side of situations.

Having a good laugh can decrease stress hormones and also increase immune cells and infection-fighting antibodies.

Laughter also triggers the release of endorphins, the body's natural feel-good chemicals. Endorphins promote an overall sense of well-being and can even temporarily relieve pain, as well as having a very positive effect on your emotional well-being.

Laughter lets me relax. It's the equivalent of taking a deep breath, letting it out and saying, 'This, too, will pass'

Odette Pollar

Help others

Helping to support other people so that they feel better about their lives can in turn be good for your mental health as well. Giving connects you to others and provides you with a sense of meaning and ultimately can create stronger communities and help build a happier society for everyone. Thinking of ways to be kind and giving to others will improve your sense of self-worth and also create some balance and perspective by encouraging you to look outwards rather than inwards.

I fight for my health
every day in a way most people
don't understand. I'm not lazy.
I'm a warrior

Unknown

Healing takes time and asking for help is a courageous step

Mariska Hargitay

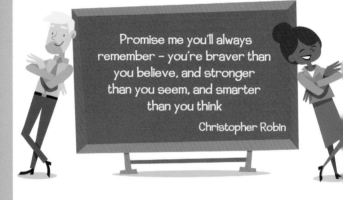

Promise me you'll always remember - you're braver than you believe, and stronger than you seem, and smarter than you think

Christopher Robin